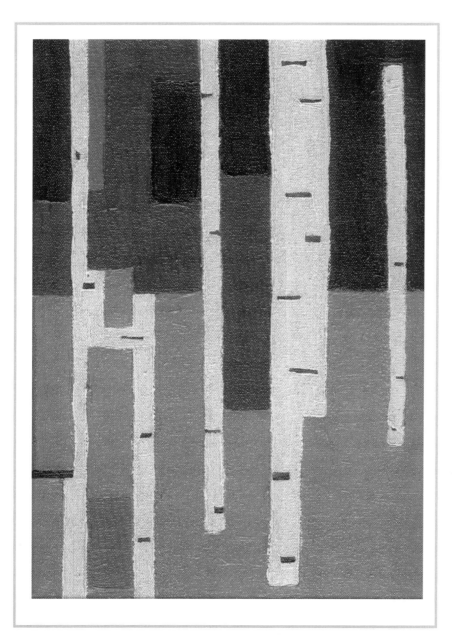

A.C.H. and T.T., *Abstraction #2 (In the Birch Grove)*, c. 1955

Stand By Your Man

or

Annie Crawford Hurn: My Life with Tom Thomson

By Andrew T. Hunter

The Edmonton Art Gallery and Art Gallery of Hamilton

Stand By Your Man

An installation and publication project by Andrew T. Hunter co-produced by
The Edmonton Art Gallery and Art GAllery of Hamilton.

Art Gallery of Hamilton
March 17 through May 27, 2001

Confederation Centre Art Gallery and Museum
June 24 through August 27, 2001

Edmonton Art Gallery
September 21, 2001 through February 2, 2002

National Library of Canada Cataloguing in Publication Data

Thomson, Tom, 1877–1917.
        Stand By Your Man

        Catalogue of an exhibition produced by The Edmonton Art Gallery, in
partnership with the Art Gallery of Hamilton.
        ISBN 0–88950–127–0

        1. Thomson, Tom, 1877–1917.   --Exhibitions   I. Hunter, Andrew, 1963–
II. Edmonton Art Gallery.   III. Art Gallery of Hamilton.IV. Title.
ND249.T5A4 2001   759.11   C2001–910281–X

For Miss Szabo, who got me started.

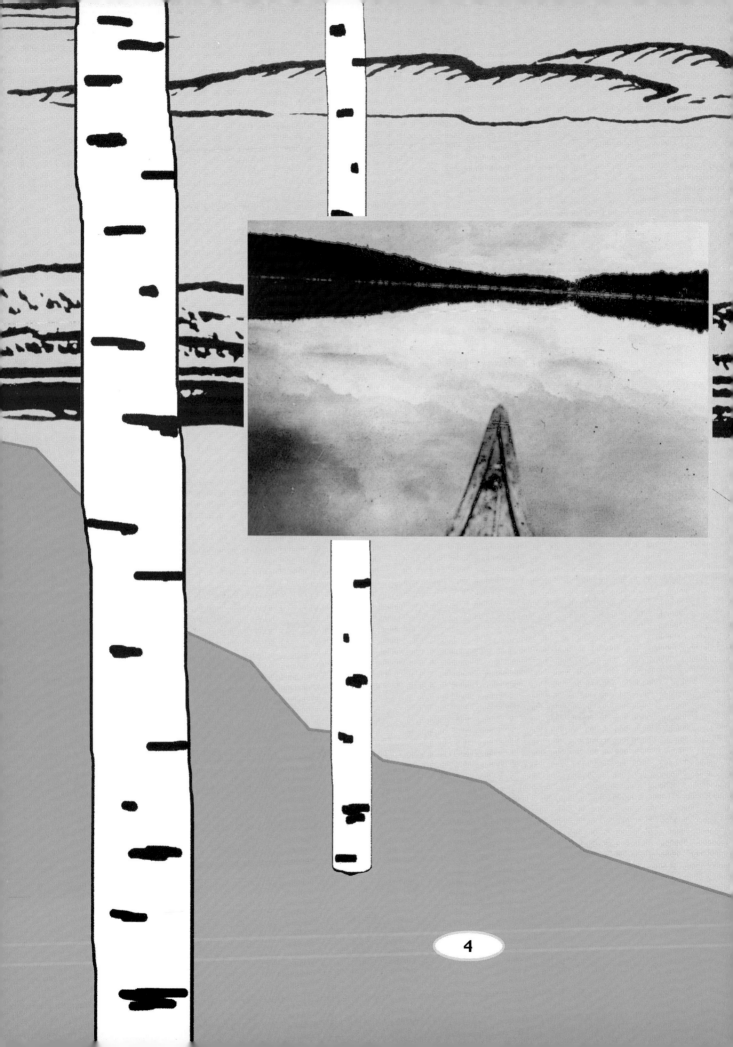

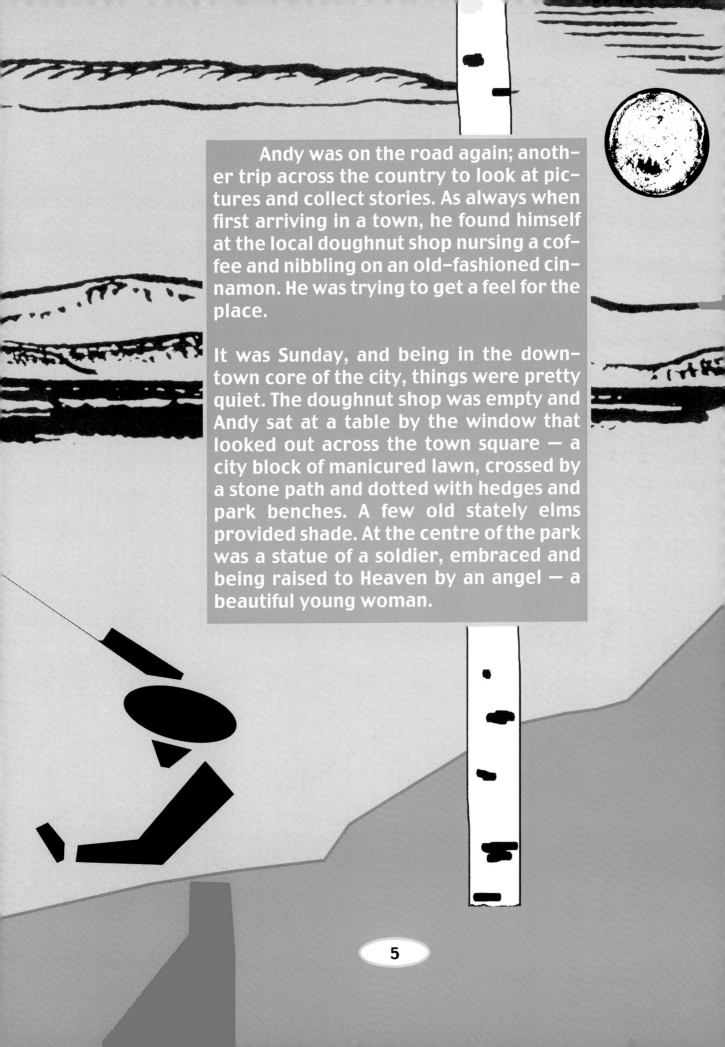

Andy was on the road again; another trip across the country to look at pictures and collect stories. As always when first arriving in a town, he found himself at the local doughnut shop nursing a coffee and nibbling on an old-fashioned cinnamon. He was trying to get a feel for the place.

It was Sunday, and being in the downtown core of the city, things were pretty quiet. The doughnut shop was empty and Andy sat at a table by the window that looked out across the town square — a city block of manicured lawn, crossed by a stone path and dotted with hedges and park benches. A few old stately elms provided shade. At the centre of the park was a statue of a soldier, embraced and being raised to Heaven by an angel — a beautiful young woman.

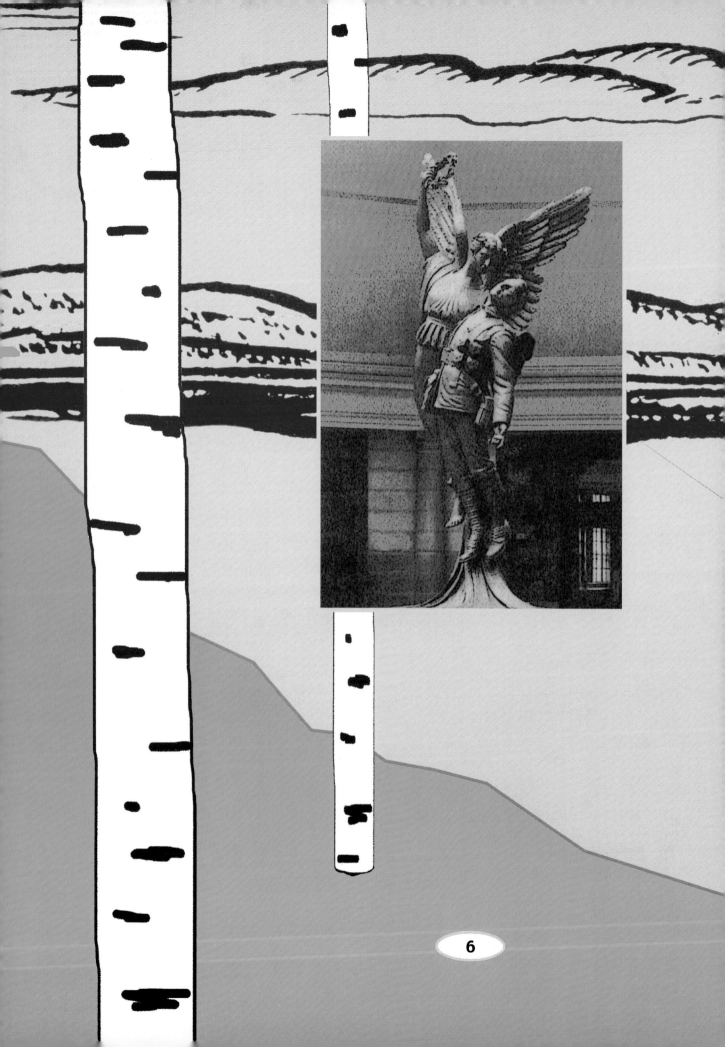

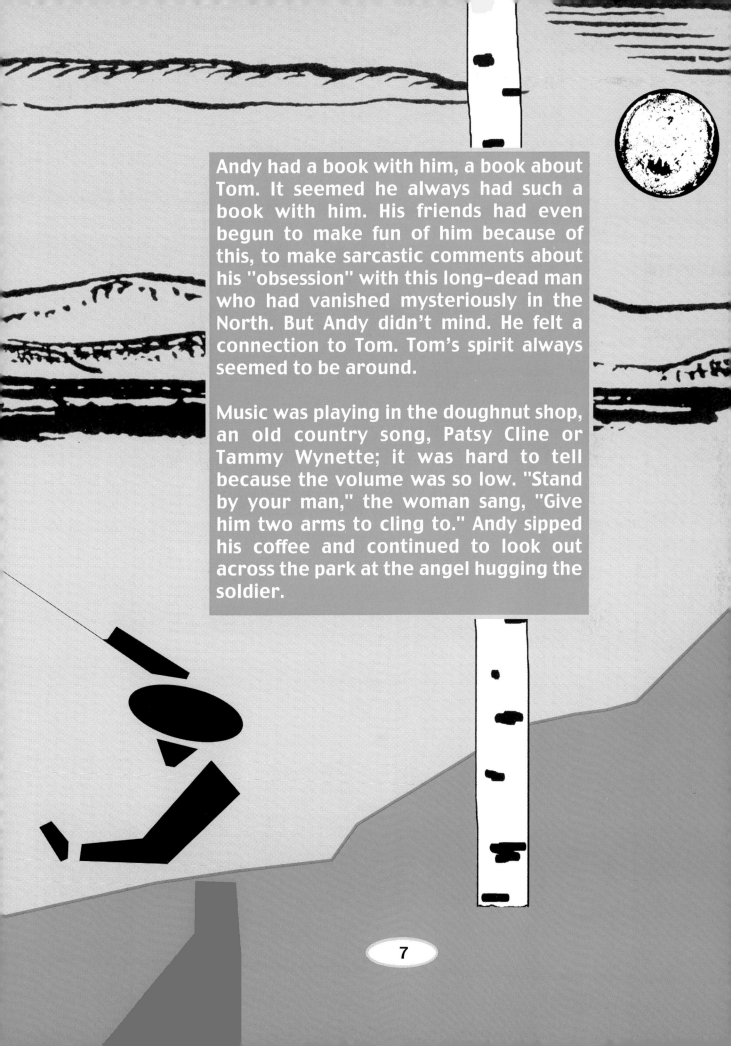

Andy had a book with him, a book about Tom. It seemed he always had such a book with him. His friends had even begun to make fun of him because of this, to make sarcastic comments about his "obsession" with this long–dead man who had vanished mysteriously in the North. But Andy didn't mind. He felt a connection to Tom. Tom's spirit always seemed to be around.

Music was playing in the doughnut shop, an old country song, Patsy Cline or Tammy Wynette; it was hard to tell because the volume was so low. "Stand by your man," the woman sang, "Give him two arms to cling to." Andy sipped his coffee and continued to look out across the park at the angel hugging the soldier.

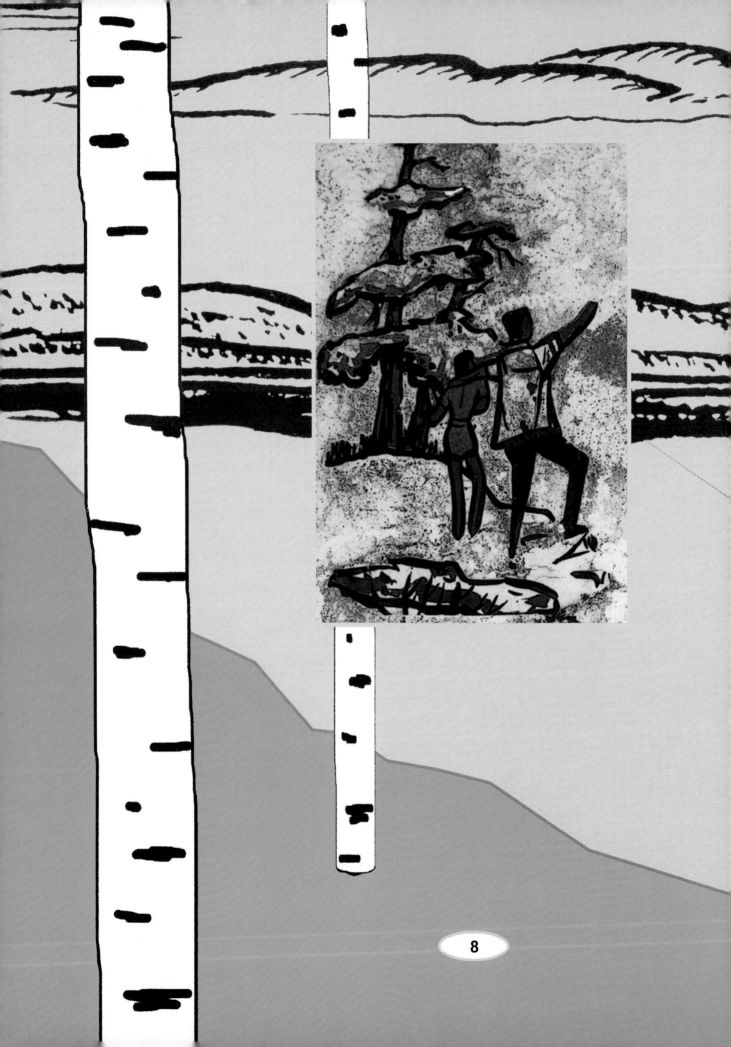

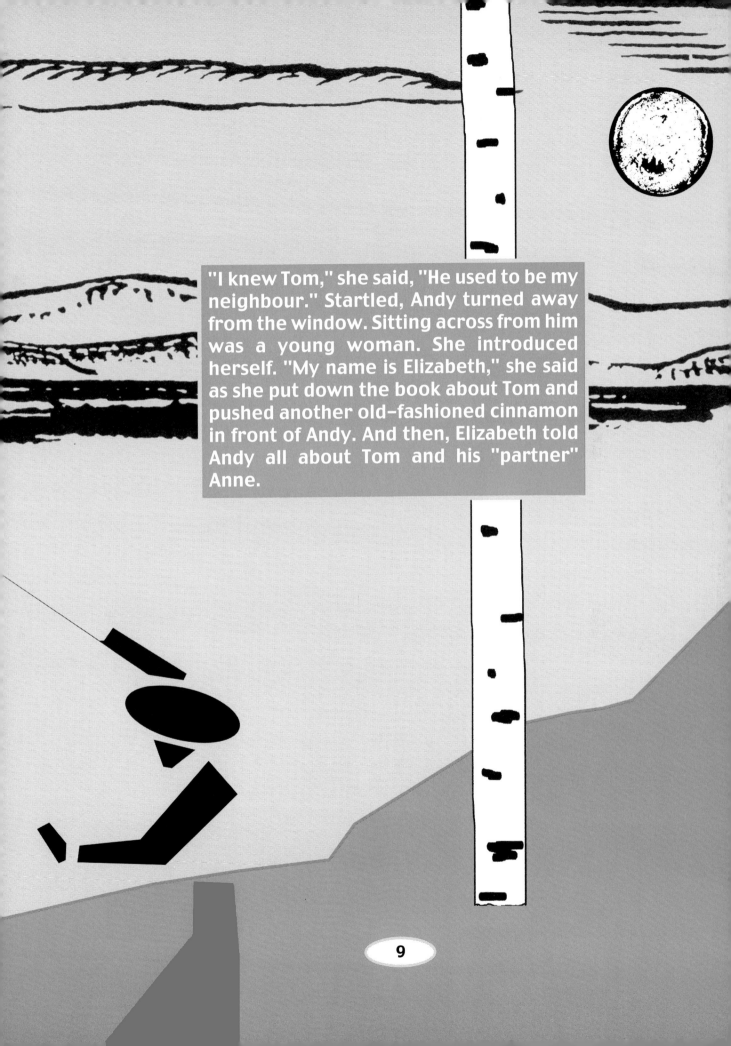

"I knew Tom," she said, "He used to be my neighbour." Startled, Andy turned away from the window. Sitting across from him was a young woman. She introduced herself. "My name is Elizabeth," she said as she put down the book about Tom and pushed another old-fashioned cinnamon in front of Andy. And then, Elizabeth told Andy all about Tom and his "partner" Anne.

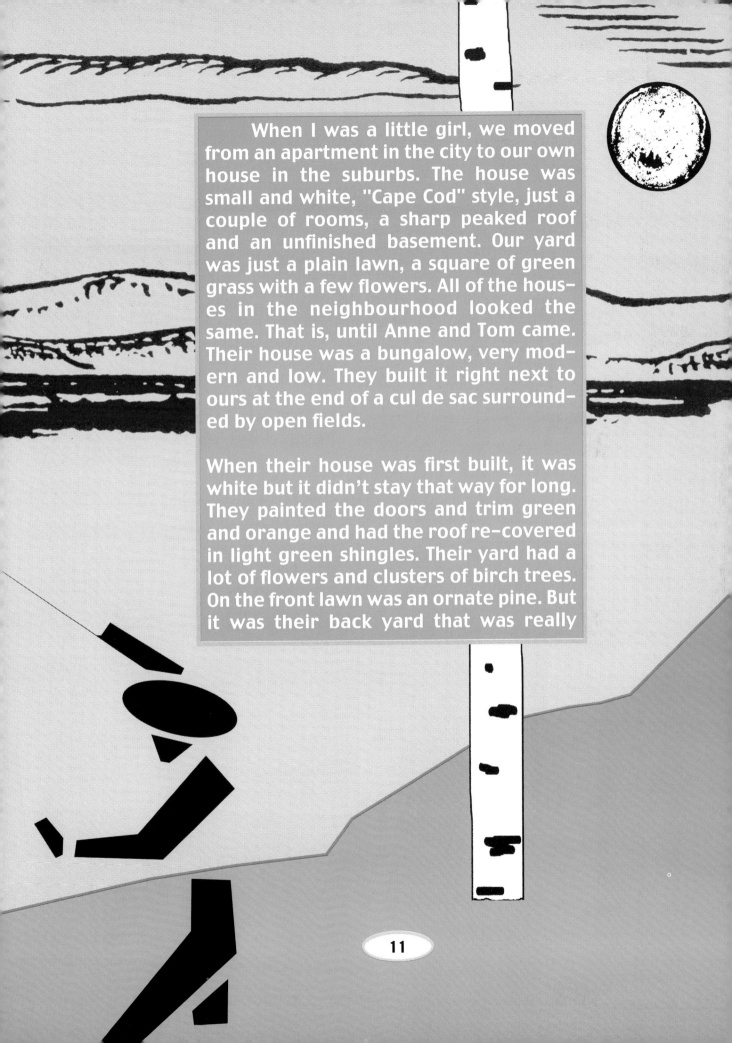

When I was a little girl, we moved from an apartment in the city to our own house in the suburbs. The house was small and white, "Cape Cod" style, just a couple of rooms, a sharp peaked roof and an unfinished basement. Our yard was just a plain lawn, a square of green grass with a few flowers. All of the houses in the neighbourhood looked the same. That is, until Anne and Tom came. Their house was a bungalow, very modern and low. They built it right next to ours at the end of a cul de sac surrounded by open fields.

When their house was first built, it was white but it didn't stay that way for long. They painted the doors and trim green and orange and had the roof re-covered in light green shingles. Their yard had a lot of flowers and clusters of birch trees. On the front lawn was an ornate pine. But it was their back yard that was really

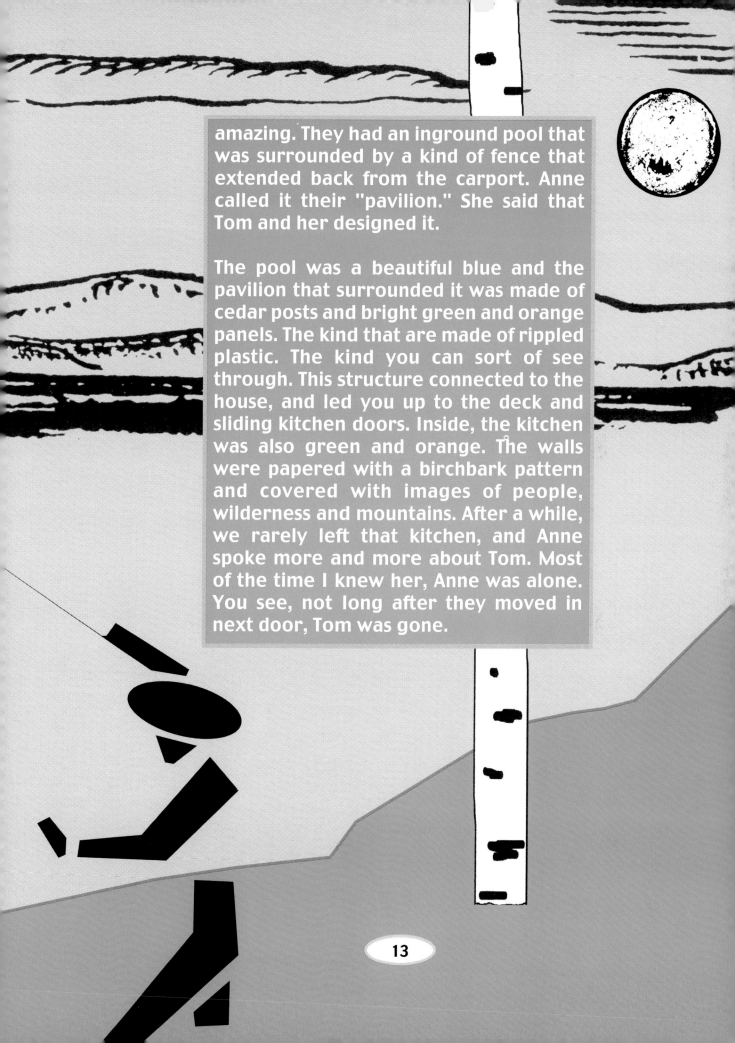

amazing. They had an inground pool that was surrounded by a kind of fence that extended back from the carport. Anne called it their "pavilion." She said that Tom and her designed it.

The pool was a beautiful blue and the pavilion that surrounded it was made of cedar posts and bright green and orange panels. The kind that are made of rippled plastic. The kind you can sort of see through. This structure connected to the house, and led you up to the deck and sliding kitchen doors. Inside, the kitchen was also green and orange. The walls were papered with a birchbark pattern and covered with images of people, wilderness and mountains. After a while, we rarely left that kitchen, and Anne spoke more and more about Tom. Most of the time I knew her, Anne was alone. You see, not long after they moved in next door, Tom was gone.

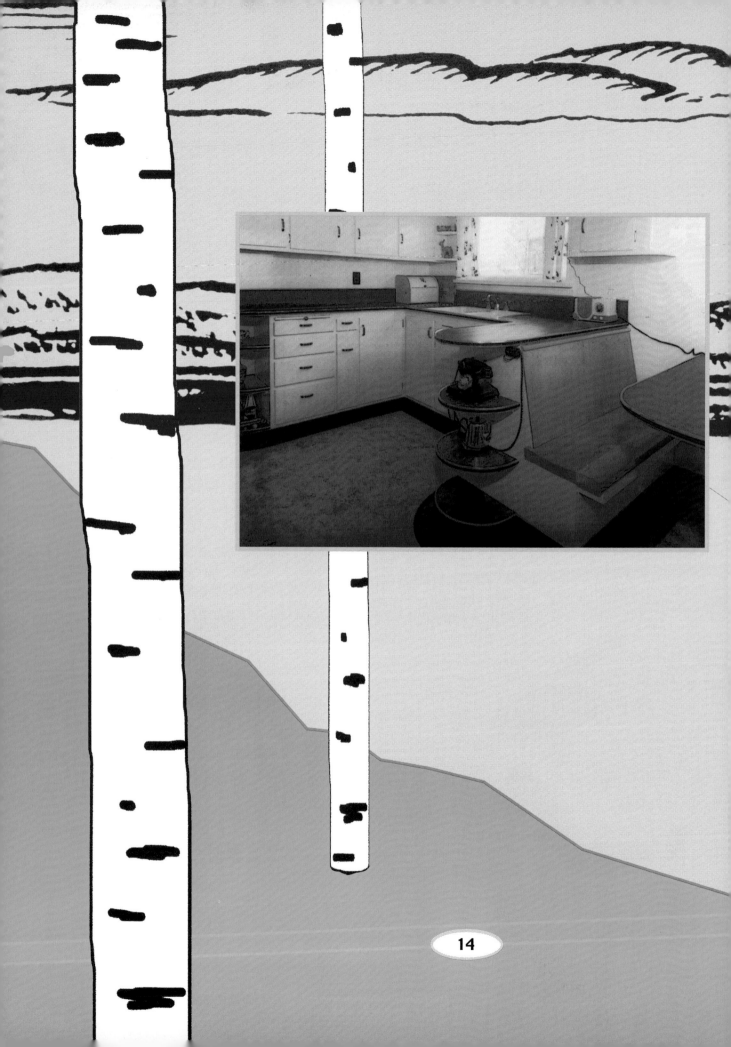

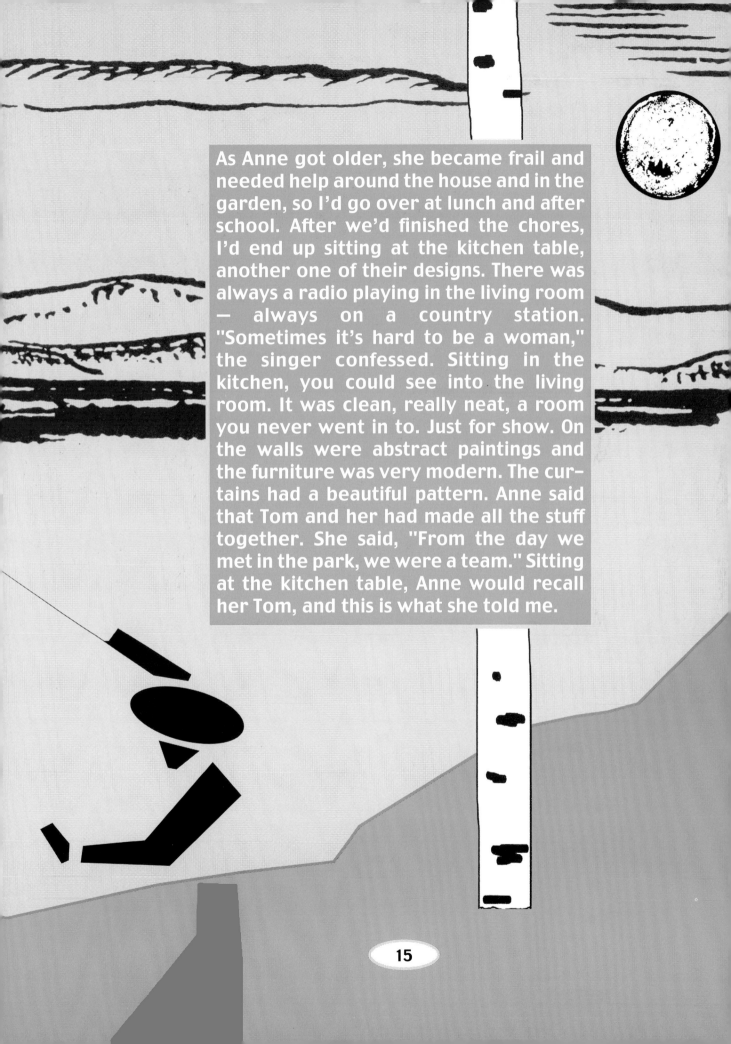

As Anne got older, she became frail and needed help around the house and in the garden, so I'd go over at lunch and after school. After we'd finished the chores, I'd end up sitting at the kitchen table, another one of their designs. There was always a radio playing in the living room — always on a country station. "Sometimes it's hard to be a woman," the singer confessed. Sitting in the kitchen, you could see into the living room. It was clean, really neat, a room you never went in to. Just for show. On the walls were abstract paintings and the furniture was very modern. The curtains had a beautiful pattern. Anne said that Tom and her had made all the stuff together. She said, "From the day we met in the park, we were a team." Sitting at the kitchen table, Anne would recall her Tom, and this is what she told me.

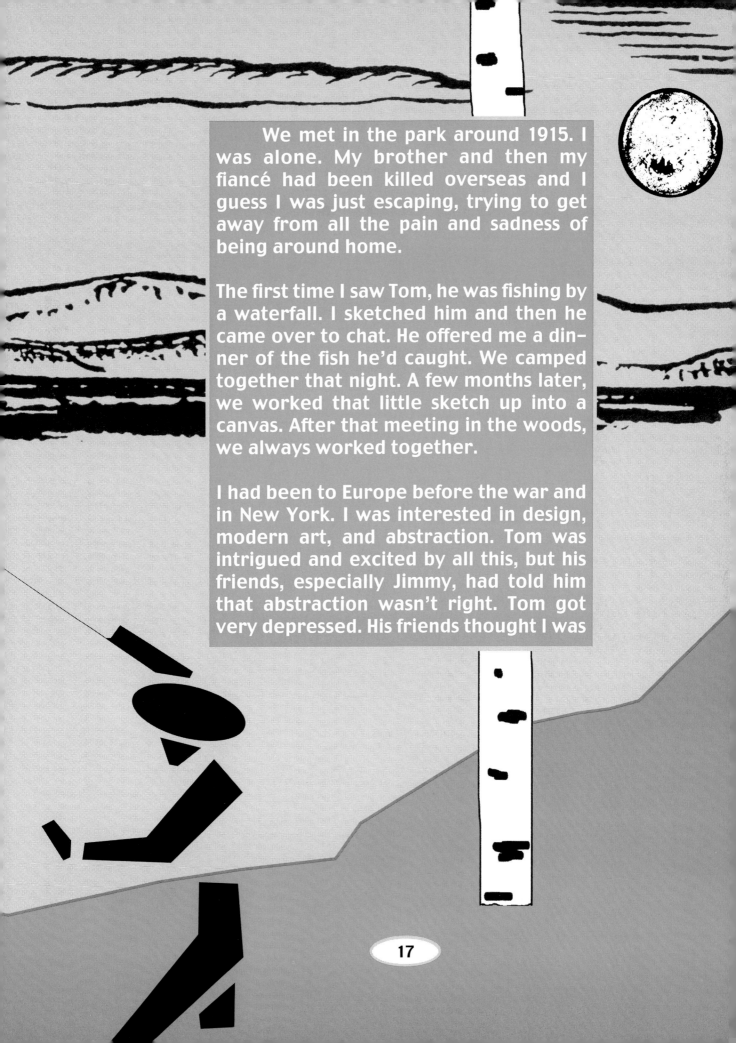

We met in the park around 1915. I was alone. My brother and then my fiancé had been killed overseas and I guess I was just escaping, trying to get away from all the pain and sadness of being around home.

The first time I saw Tom, he was fishing by a waterfall. I sketched him and then he came over to chat. He offered me a din-ner of the fish he'd caught. We camped together that night. A few months later, we worked that little sketch up into a canvas. After that meeting in the woods, we always worked together.

I had been to Europe before the war and in New York. I was interested in design, modern art, and abstraction. Tom was intrigued and excited by all this, but his friends, especially Jimmy, had told him that abstraction wasn't right. Tom got very depressed. His friends thought I was

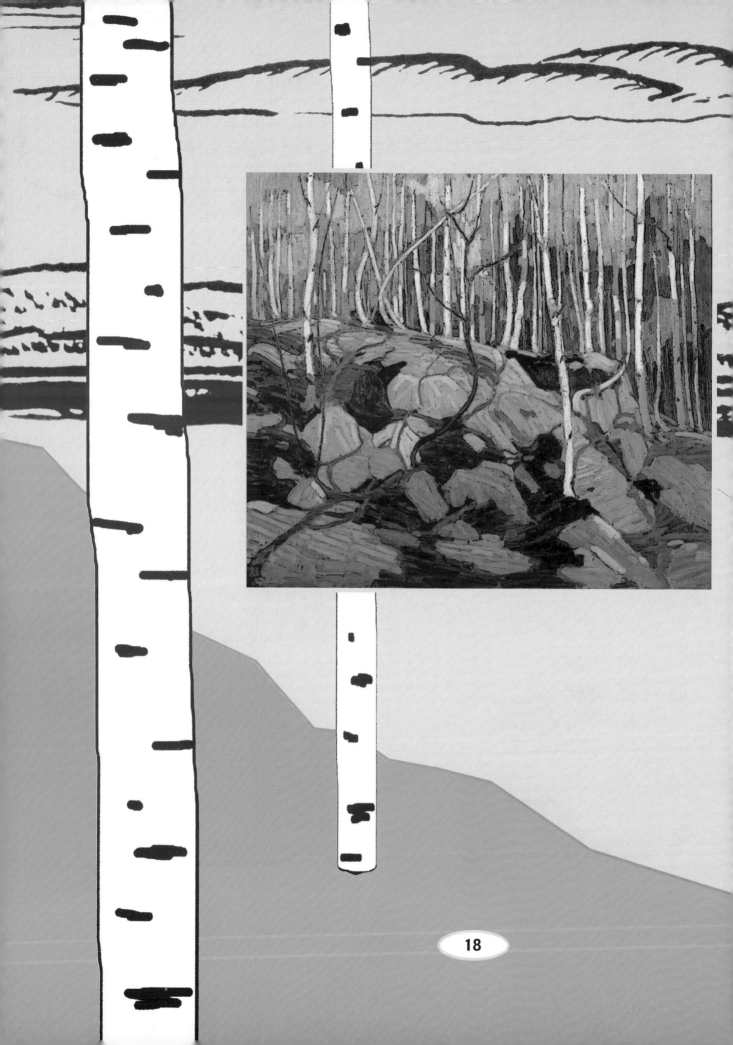

a bad influence and Tom began to feel that they were trying to control him. He felt trapped because they had done so much to get him started. Like me, Tom was looking to escape. He wanted us to go out west. He wanted to explore a new way of making art. And that's when it appeared. It was terrifying, but Tom saw it as the way out, his path to freedom.

We were in the cabin, sitting by the table. It was late and I had just finished my tea and was thinking of going to bed. Tom sat staring into his cup, the smoke from his pipe a faint blue thread. He had been pretty quiet all night, even when we were working on one of the birch paint-ings together. When he looked up at me, it was startling; his gaze was so intense. Then he looked over at the birch grove painting and Tom told me about what he'd seen, what he'd met that day in the woods.

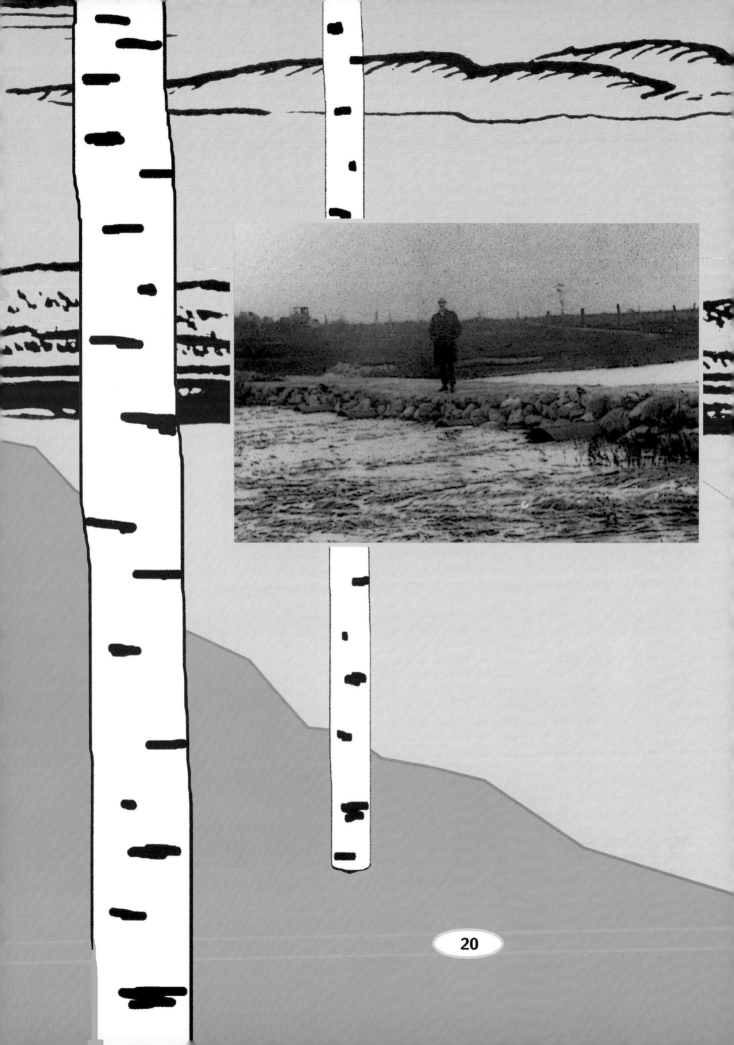

Those dogs seem to have been fol-
lowing me around all summer, all shaggy
and unkempt, lurking in the woods or
along the edge of the lake. Always
together, like a single beast.

Today, while I sat in the woods sketching
a deep grove of birches, they came up to
me. They sniffed around my boots and
paint box and then, after circling a few
times, sat together in front of me, block-
ing the view. I put down my brush. Then I
heard a voice.

It was the same voice I'd heard when I
was a boy. I was fishing near the old
farm, down by the river that ran into
town. He appeared on the stone road
that they'd built across the water; a big
man in a dark coat and hat. He appeared
out of thin air. He said, "Tell me where
you want to go." I said, "Well, y'know, I

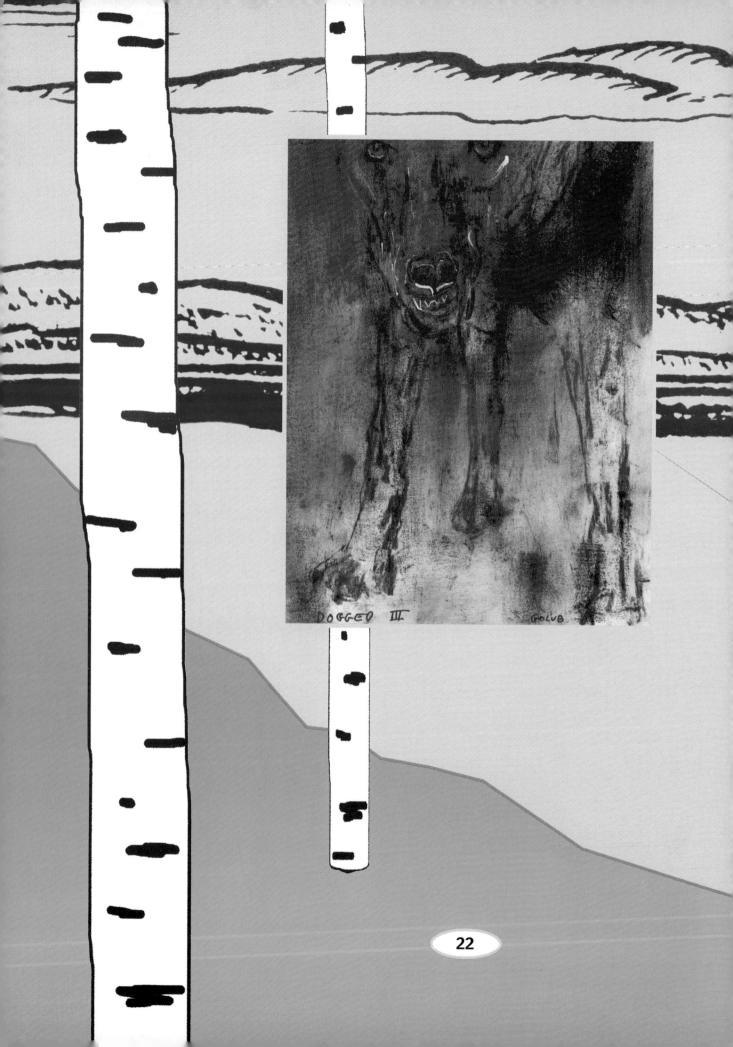

DOGGED III   GOLUB

just want to get away." He said, " I can do that, but there'll be a price."

"Your time is up," the voice said as the dogs stared me down. I stood up and pleaded, "But I'm not finished yet. There's somewhere else I want to go." "And where is that?" came the voice, as the dogs shifted and whispered a faint growl. "Out west, to the mountains," I said, "I want to leave this behind. I want to be with Anne. I want to stop making just pictures. I want to create something new. I want to build a home" The voice said, " I can do that, but there'll be a price."

Tomorrow I'm going fishing Anne. Please wait for me.

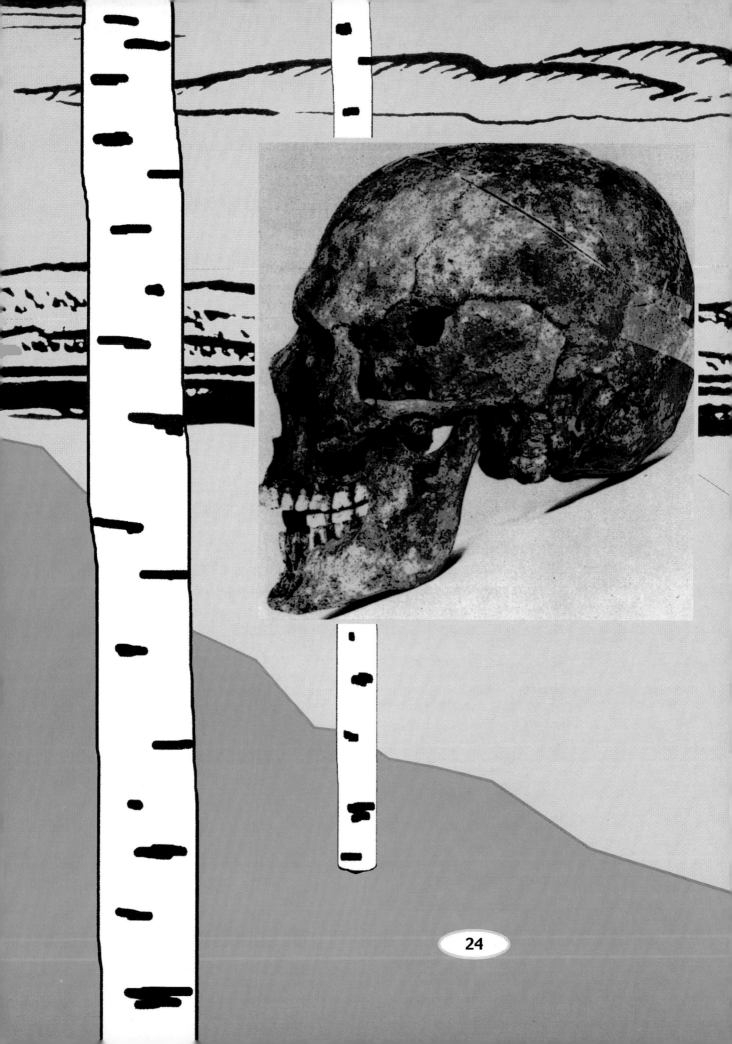

In the morning, Tom was gone. I looked out and saw his canoe was missing. Later that day they found it capsized on the lake. I waited by the cabin for a week. There was a lot of commotion around the lake and then I heard that they'd found Tom's body. They said he'd drowned. I kept waiting for Tom.

The dogs appeared in the morning. They came down the back hill out of the woods while I was sitting on the porch. They circled around me, woofing softly. I followed them to Tom's grave. I kept waiting for Tom.

The dogs left. The ground stirred. Two hands pushed their way up through the soft soil followed by long muscular arms. I reached out and grabbed his hands. Tom pulled himself up out of the ground. He looked taller, stronger, and younger. "Thanks for waiting," he said as he

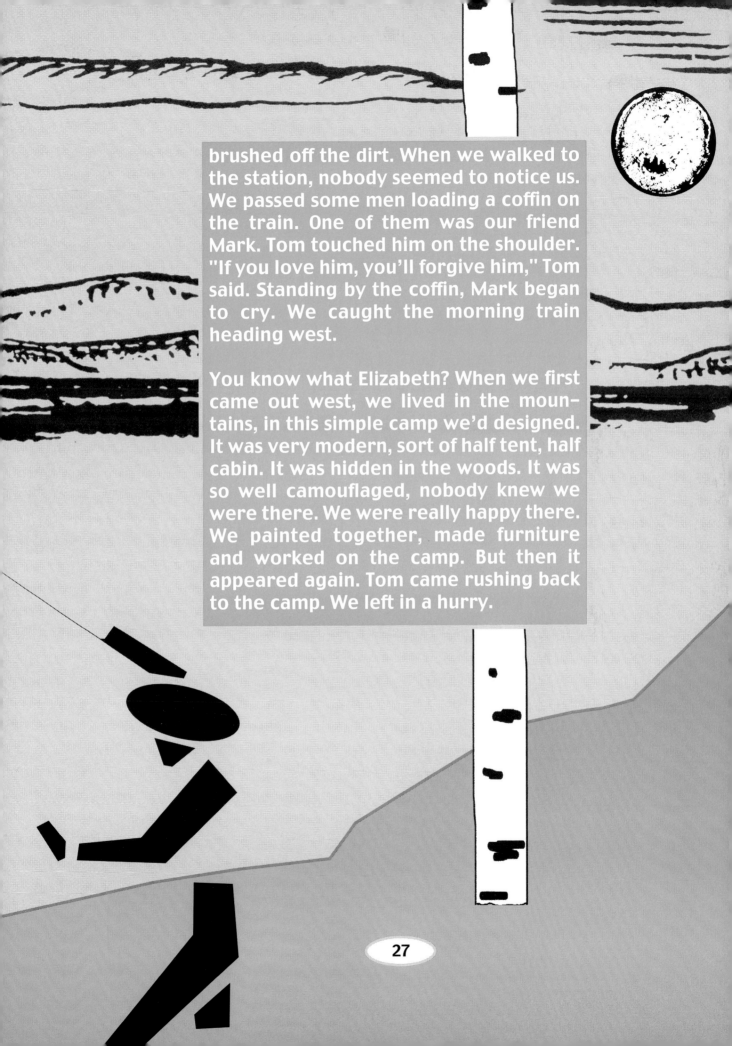

brushed off the dirt. When we walked to the station, nobody seemed to notice us. We passed some men loading a coffin on the train. One of them was our friend Mark. Tom touched him on the shoulder. "If you love him, you'll forgive him," Tom said. Standing by the coffin, Mark began to cry. We caught the morning train heading west.

You know what Elizabeth? When we first came out west, we lived in the moun-tains, in this simple camp we'd designed. It was very modern, sort of half tent, half cabin. It was hidden in the woods. It was so well camouflaged, nobody knew we were there. We were really happy there. We painted together, made furniture and worked on the camp. But then it appeared again. Tom came rushing back to the camp. We left in a hurry.

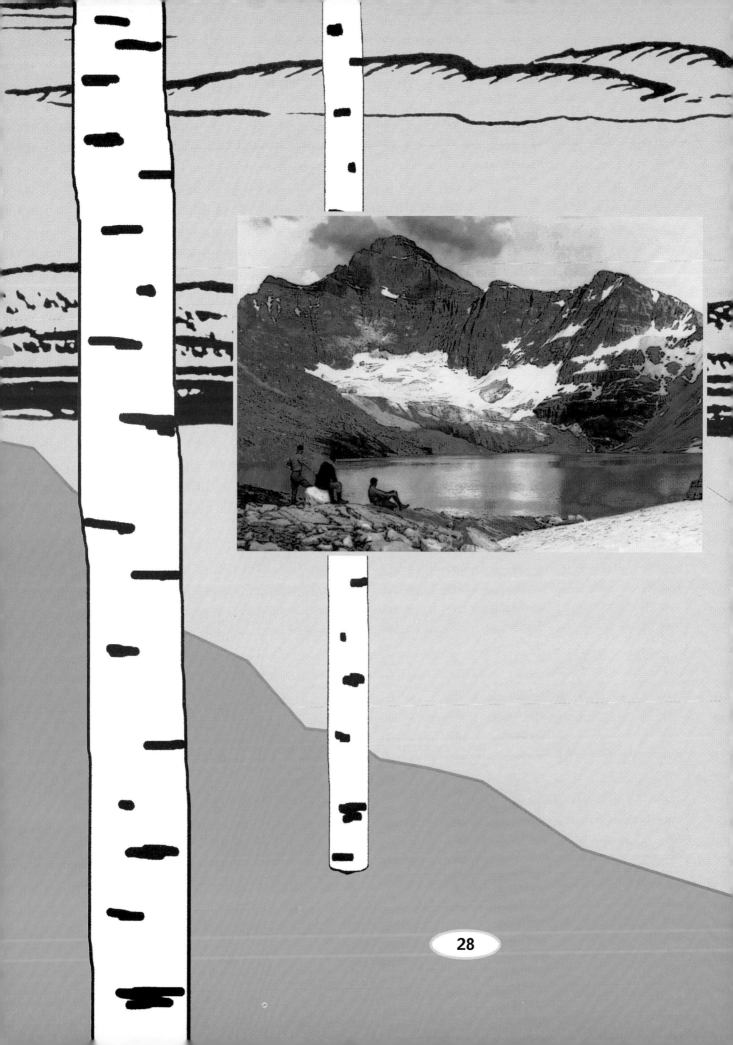

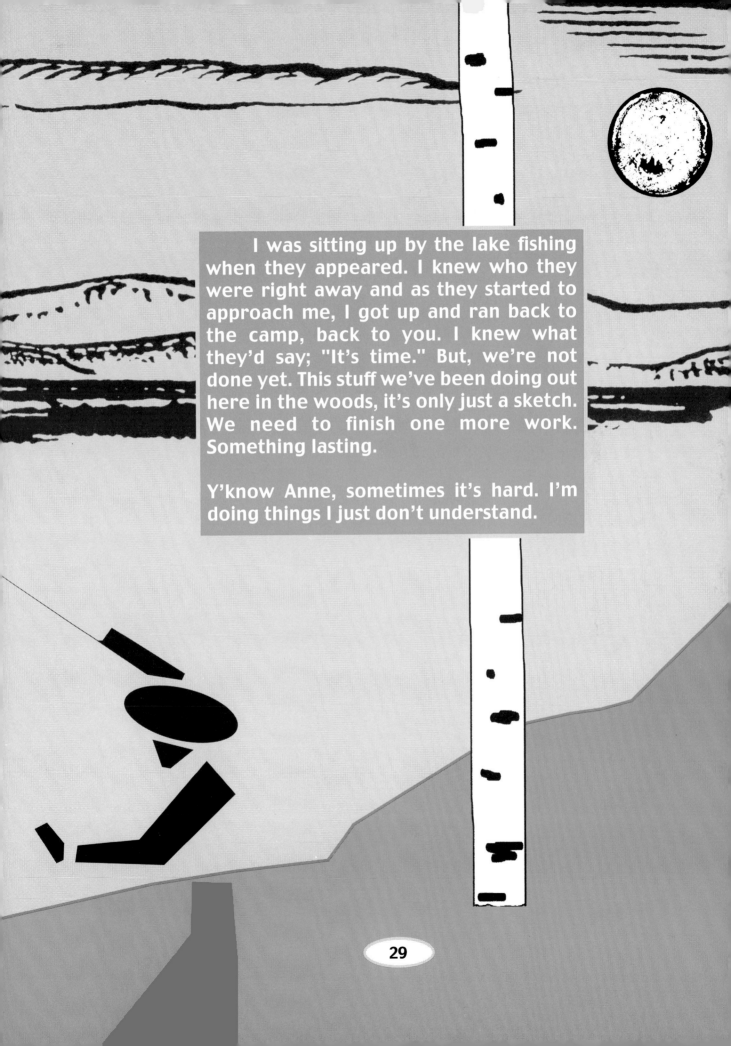

I was sitting up by the lake fishing when they appeared. I knew who they were right away and as they started to approach me, I got up and ran back to the camp, back to you. I knew what they'd say; "It's time." But, we're not done yet. This stuff we've been doing out here in the woods, it's only just a sketch. We need to finish one more work. Something lasting.

Y'know Anne, sometimes it's hard. I'm doing things I just don't understand.

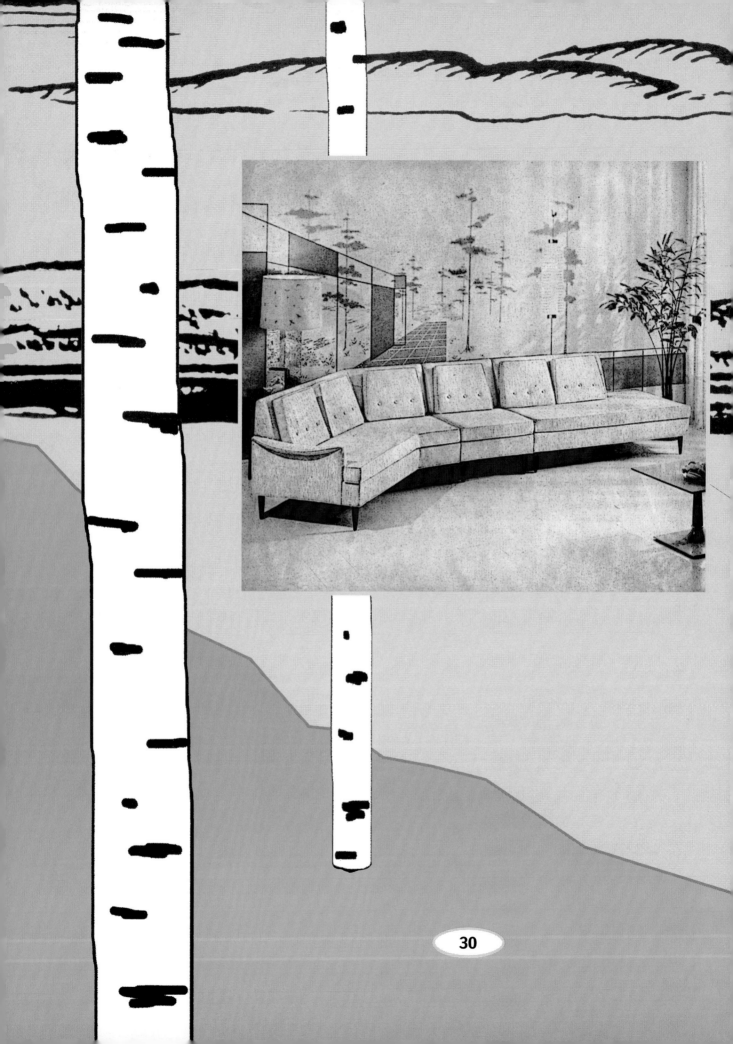

Tom saw the ad in the paper. The Highlands it was called. "Where Pleasure and Health combine for Happiness," the ad claimed. We had them build the most modern design they had, a low bungalow, and then we set about to make it our own. We remodeled the interior, laid out the gardens and built the pavilion with the pool. The furniture was a combination of things we'd made and a few select items we'd ordered. It was all coming together, almost finished, but Tom never seemed to settle. He was edgy. He knew time was short. If he wasn't working on the house, he would stand at the front window watching the street, waiting for it to come. Tom started to look very old.

We got a big black dog, thought it might scare things off or warn of visitors, but it just made us both tense. Whenever the dog barked, we'd panic. Funny, when it

finally came, that dog never made a sound.

The doorbell rang. Tom was out by the pool. I answered it. She was a tall woman with a dark coat and hat. I thought she was a salesperson. She stepped into the living room and looked around. She smiled, said she liked what she saw, especially the abstract painting of the birches we'd just finished that hung over the fireplace. She said, "You've done a beautiful job on this house." I told her it had taken a long time. "A lifetime," she said with a grin.

She walked past me and through the kitchen to the sliding glass doors. "What beautiful flowers," she commented as her eyes searched the yard, "and I love what you've done with the fence around the pool." I told her we thought of it as a pavilion. "Yes," she said, pointing at the overhang that extended off the carport

to shade the pool; "I see what you mean."

She stood at the door for a while in silence until I asked her what she was selling. "Nothing," she said as she stepped out onto the deck and walked over to the pool, "I'm afraid I have nothing left to sell."

I stood with her poolside and looked at the dark shape that floated in the water. Tom was floating just below the surface face down. She grabbed the skimmer, and I watched in silence as she drew him to the edge then reached in and lifted him out of the water. She cradled him in her arms.

"Sometimes it's hard," she said, "Giving all your love to just one man." Then, she just walked around the pool and out of sight behind the pavilion.

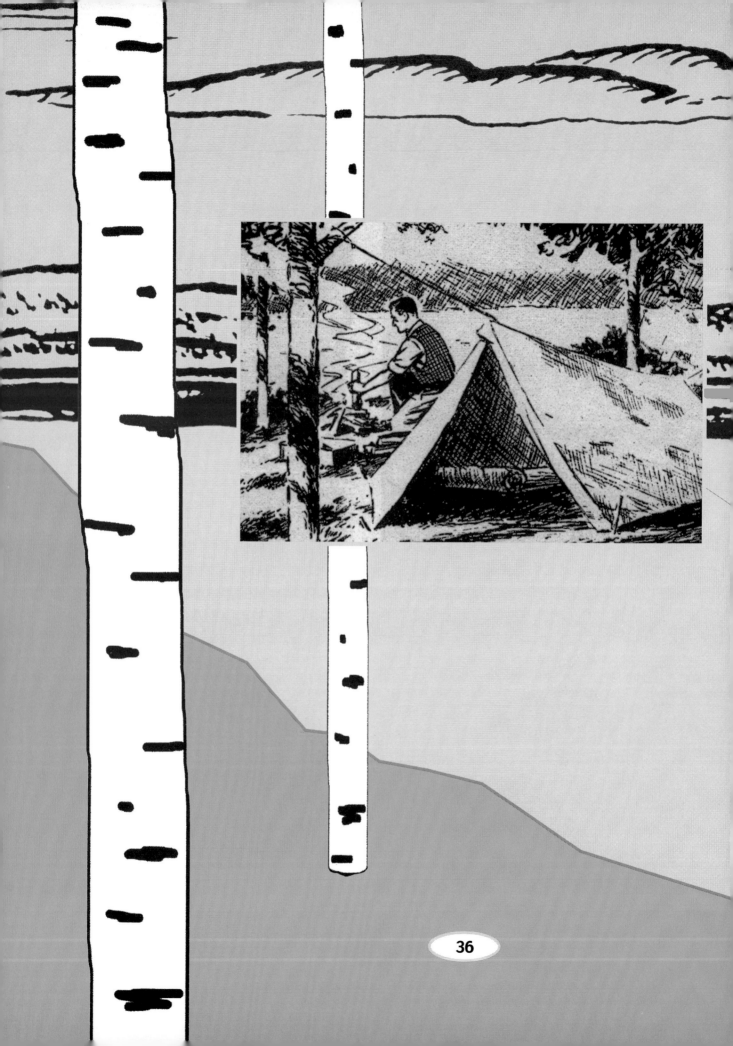

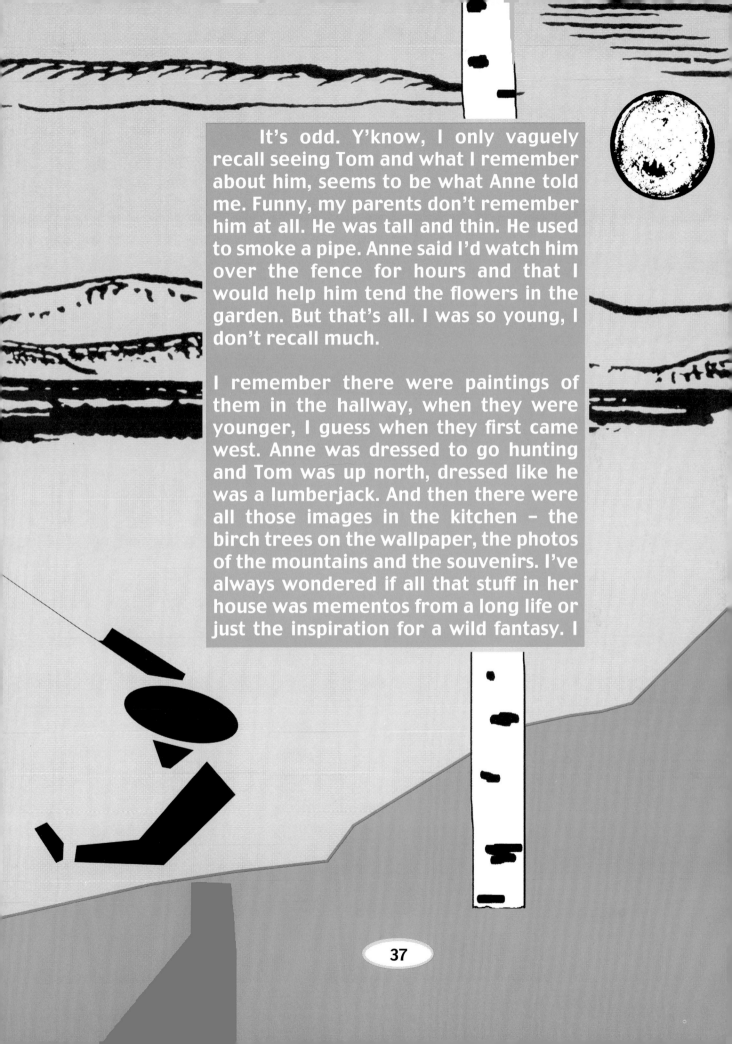

It's odd. Y'know, I only vaguely recall seeing Tom and what I remember about him, seems to be what Anne told me. Funny, my parents don't remember him at all. He was tall and thin. He used to smoke a pipe. Anne said I'd watch him over the fence for hours and that I would help him tend the flowers in the garden. But that's all. I was so young, I don't recall much.

I remember there were paintings of them in the hallway, when they were younger, I guess when they first came west. Anne was dressed to go hunting and Tom was up north, dressed like he was a lumberjack. And then there were all those images in the kitchen – the birch trees on the wallpaper, the photos of the mountains and the souvenirs. I've always wondered if all that stuff in her house was mementos from a long life or just the inspiration for a wild fantasy. I

don't know. That story Anne told sure seemed real to her.

I'll never forget that house. It inspired me. Who'd have thought that would happen, living out there in the suburbs? The paintings, the furniture, the wallpaper and fabrics, and that yard, that beautiful pool and amazing pavilion. It's why I do what I do now.

Andy picked up the little map that Elizabeth had scrawled on the back of a doughnut bag. It showed a few streets and arrows marking the route to "Highland Court." He got a coffee to go and a few more doughnuts for the road.

Andy stood at the end of the road, before faded grass and patches of melting snow. There was no house, the lot sliced away by a new highway. There were clusters of birch trees and a lone, wind-swept pine tree that clung to a little island of lawn that edged the dense flow of traffic. In the ditch by the chain link fence that ran beside the highway, Andy could see a jumble of cedar posts and cracked fiber-glass panels.

He heard barking coming from behind the last house on the street, a plain white cottage with a sharp peaked roof. Andy

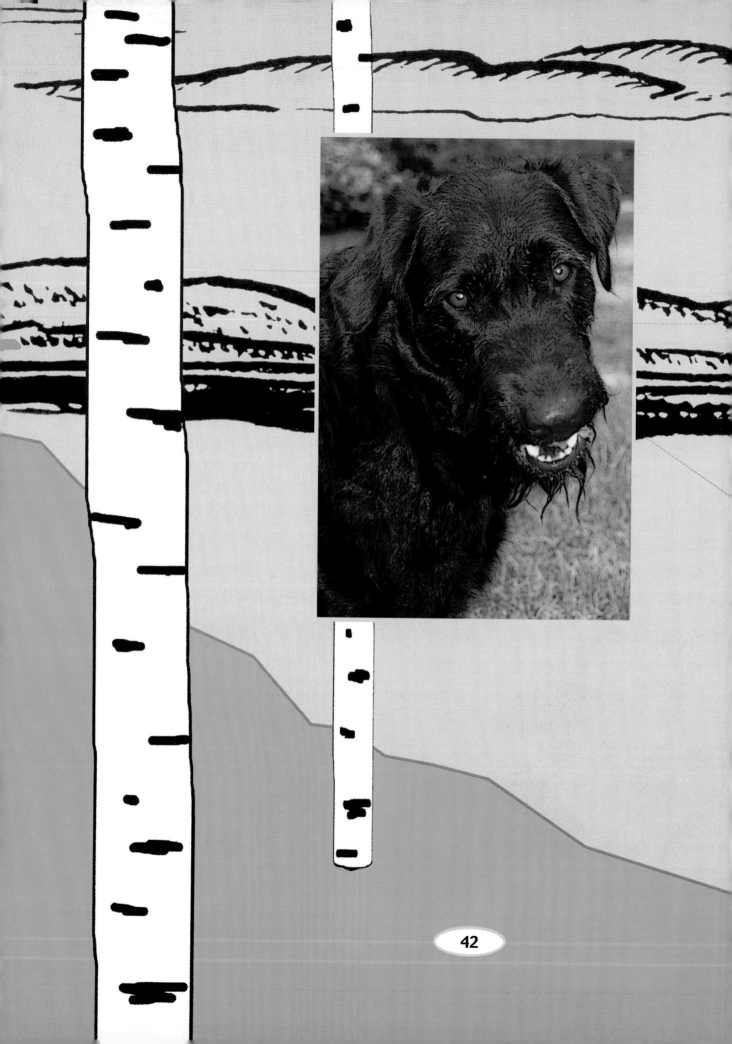

walked around back. There were four dogs held in a fenced enclosure that extended off the carport. The metal sides of an old pool lay crumpled under the weight of wet snow. At the back of the yard was a low building, a flat-roofed garden shed with a green door, its window covered by a faded orange curtain.

The air in the shed was pungent, a mix of raw earth, oil paint and gasoline. A piece of plywood, cracked and splintered, its surface spattered with paint, leaned against the back wall beside an old canvas tent, its folds stained by mildew. Andy felt colder in here than out in the yard – cold and lonely.

The dogs were out of their pen. Andy could hear them circling the shed. A big black dog filled the doorway, but as he stepped towards it, it turned and walked back to the house. The other dogs followed.

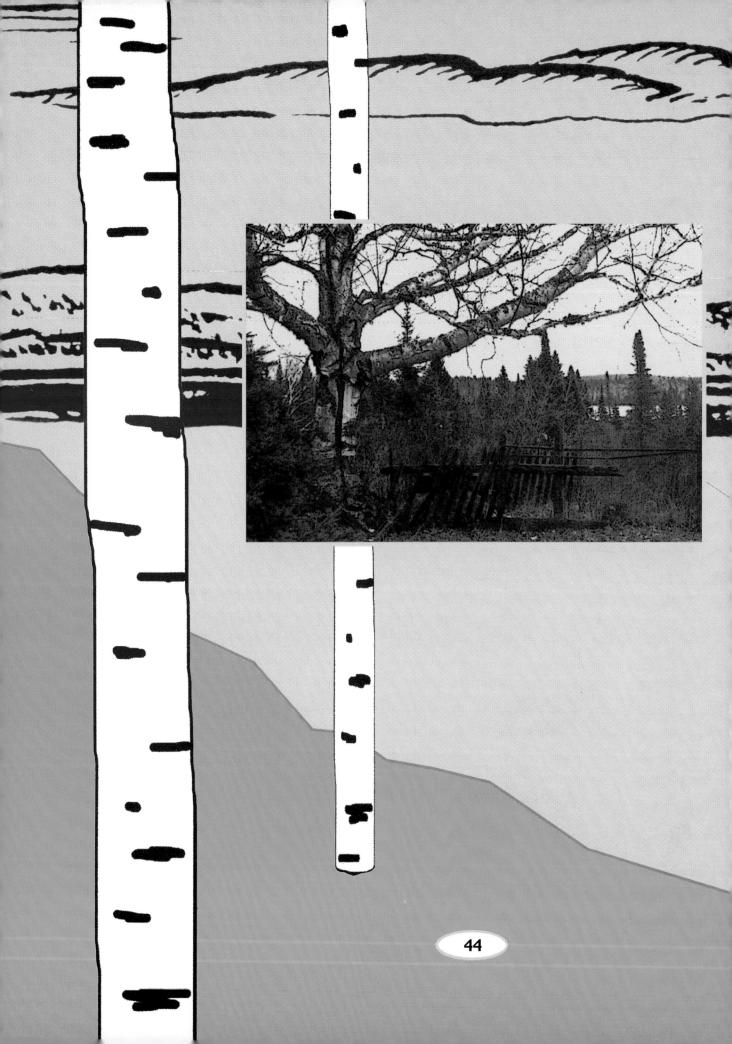

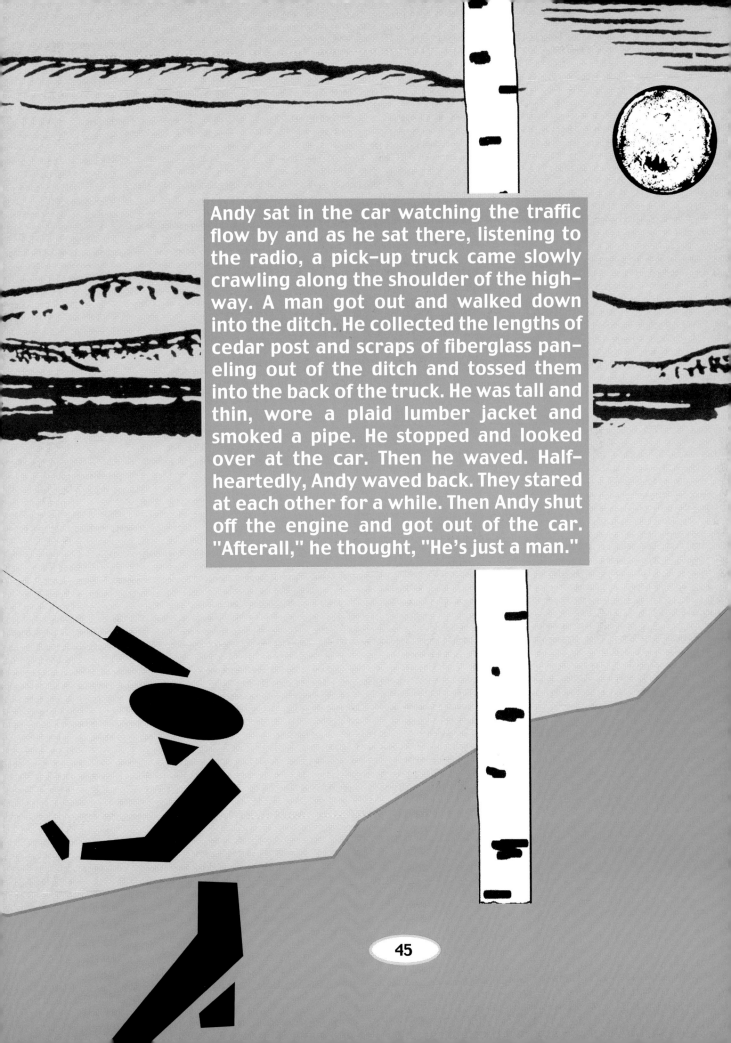

Andy sat in the car watching the traffic flow by and as he sat there, listening to the radio, a pick-up truck came slowly crawling along the shoulder of the highway. A man got out and walked down into the ditch. He collected the lengths of cedar post and scraps of fiberglass paneling out of the ditch and tossed them into the back of the truck. He was tall and thin, wore a plaid lumber jacket and smoked a pipe. He stopped and looked over at the car. Then he waved. Halfheartedly, Andy waved back. They stared at each other for a while. Then Andy shut off the engine and got out of the car. "Afterall," he thought, "He's just a man."

Andrew T. Hunter is an independent artist, writer and curator based in Dundas, Ontario. He has produced contemporary and historical exhibitions, publications and writings for public art galleries and artist-run centres across Canada and in the United States and has held curatorial positions at the Art Gallery of Hamilton, Kamloops Art Gallery and Vancouver Art Gallery.

Hunter's installation/publication projects to date include: *The Tourist* (Art Gallery of Peel, 1996), *Up North: A Northern Ontario Tragedy* (Tom Thomson Memorial Art Gallery, McMaster Museum of Art, Winnipeg Art Gallery and Kamloops Art Gallery, 1997–98), *Convergence* (Winnipeg Art Gallery and Art Gallery of Peel, 1998), *Billy's Vision* (Mendel Art Gallery, Dunlop Art Gallery, National Gallery of Canada and Walter Phillips Gallery, 2000–2002) and *Ding Ho/Group of 7* (with Gu Xiong, McMichael Canadian Art Collection and Mendel Art Gallery, 2000–2001).

In collaboration with Sarah Abbott, Hunter is currently completing *The Ascension of Billy*, a documentary film being coproduced by The Banff Centre for the Arts. His installation and book project *In the Pines* will open at the Macdonald Stewart Art Centre in the fall of 2001.

Stand By Your Man was produced by The Edmonton Art Gallery and the Art Gallery of Hamilton with the generous assistance of the Museums Assistance Program of Canadian Heritage.

Stand By Your Man was presented in Edmonton with the sponsorship of The Edmonton Regional Airports Authority and CFRN Radio. The Edmonton Art Gallery gratefully acknowledges the ongoing support of the Alberta Foundation for the Arts, The Canada Council for the Arts and the City of Edmonton. The Art Gallery of Hamilton gratefully acknowledges the support of the City of Hamilton, the Ontario Arts Council, the Canada Council for the Arts and its members and friends.

Design: Andrew T. Hunter
Design Assistance: Alan Flint
Printed at: Cascade International, Hamilton

IMAGES
Andrew T. Hunter: cover, frontispiece, page 2, 6 and 42
Lisa Hunter: page 3, 8, 30, 32, 34, 36, 38 and back cover
National Archives of Canada: page 4
University of Guelph: page 20

TOM THOMSON PAINTINGS

The Fisherman, nd
oil on canvas
51.3 x 56.5 cm.
The Edmonton Art Gallery, donated by Mrs. Curtis B. Munson, in memory of her husband, 1982 (82.22)
Photography: Harry Korol
page 16

The Birch Grove Autumn, 1916-17
oil on canvas
101.6 x 116.8 cm
Art Gallery of Hamilton. Gift of Roy G. Cole, Esq., in memory of his parents Matthew and Annie Bell Gilmore Cole, 1967 (1967.112.Z)
page 18

OTHER WORKS

A.C.H. and T.T.
Abstraction (In the Birch Grove), c. 1955
oil on canvas
Collection of A.T. Hunter
cover image

Andrew T. Hunter
Cabin in the Woods (after J.E.H. MacDonald), 2001
digital photograph
Collection of the artist
page 2

Maggie Hunter
Full Moon, 2001
potato print on paper
Collection of the artist
pages 5-45

Leon Golub
Dogged IV, 2000
acrylic and conté on card
Collection of the artist
page 22

Hubert Ropp
Portrait of Mrs. Edith Munson, n.d.
oil on canvas
102 x 77 cm
The Edmonton Art Gallery Collection, donated by Mrs. Curtis B. Munson, in memory of her husband, 1982 (82.22)
Photography: Harry Korol
page 46 (top)

Yulia Biriukova
The Riverman Frenchy Renaud, 1935
oil on canvas
122.1 x 106.9 cm
Gift of Thoreau MacDonald, Esq., 1973 (74.43.2)
page 46 (bottom)